What Is a Sentence?

A **sentence** is a group of words that tell a complete thought. A sentence tells who or what is doing something and what happens.

kicks the ball	Josie kicks the ball.
This is not a sentence. This group of words does not tell who is doing something.	This is a sentence. It tells who is doing something and what she is doing.

Write *yes* if the words make a sentence.
Write *no* if the words do not make a sentence.

1. The game started on time. _____

2. The other team. _____

3. Then Ally made a goal. _____

4. I fell over the ball. _____

5. Cheered for their team. _____

6. Flew into the net. _____

7. Jason was our goalie. _____

8. The crowd in the stands. _____

9. Cheered after we won. _____

0. We will play again next week. _____

© ... pany

D1416703

What Is a Subject?

The **subject** tells who or what the sentence is about. A **simple subject** tells about one person or thing. A **compound subject** tells about more than one person or thing.

Jorge plays the drums.

Jorge tells who this sentence is about. *Jorge* is a simple subject because it names only one person.

Drums and guitars are my favorite instruments.

Drums and guitars are a compound subject because they name more than one thing.

Underline the subject in each sentence. Circle *s* or *c* to show whether the subject is simple or compound.

1. Mr. Ramirez leads our school band.   s   c

2. The band plays at all the home games.   s   c

3. Cory and Rosa play the clarinet.   s   c

4. Jeannette teaches us how to march in step. s   c

5. Leroy and his brother play the trumpet.   s   c

6. The bus takes us to games across town.   s   c

7. Our driver knows all our school songs.   s   c

8. Once Mia and I forgot our band uniforms.   s   c

9. Parents and students come to many games.   s   c

10. They like to hear the band play.   s   c

©1999 School Zone Publishing Company

What Is a Predicate?

The **predicate** is the sentence part that tells what the subject does. The predicate always contains a verb.

> The lion **hides** in the tall grass.

The words *hides in the tall grass* tell what the lion does. *Hides* is the verb.

A **simple predicate** tells about one thing the subject does. A **compound predicate** tells more than one thing the subject does.

> The zebras **saw** the lion.

The words *saw the lion* are a simple predicate because they tell about one thing the subject did.

> The lion **leaped** up and **chased** the zebras.

The words *leaped up and chased the zebras* are a compound predicate because they tell about two things the subject did.

Underline the predicate in each sentence. Circle *s* or *c* to show whether the predicate is simple or compound.

1. The sea turtle crawled out of the ocean.   s   c

2. She dug in the sand and laid her eggs.   s   c

3. Then she covered the eggs with sand.   s   c

4. The sun shone on the sand and warmed the eggs.   s   c

5. A snake dug up an egg and ate it.   s   c

6. People took some eggs for soup.   s   c

7. The rest of the eggs finally hatched.   s   c

8. The baby turtles climbed out of the sand.   s   c

9. They ran down the sand and swam into the sea.   s   c

0. Later they will come back and lay eggs.   s   c

©1999 School Zone Publishing Company

What Is a Compound Sentence?

A **compound sentence** is two or more sentences joined by a comma and the word *and* or *but*.

The bus broke down. We were late for school.
The bus broke down, and we were late for school.

We were hungry. The cafeteria was closed.
We were hungry, but the cafeteria was closed.

If a pair of sentences makes sense together, write a compound sentence using a comma and the word *and* or *but*. If the sentences do not make sense together, write *not a compound sentence*.

1. I like pizza. I hate mushrooms on it.

   _____

2. Greg dislikes pizza. He doesn't like hot dogs either.

   _____

3. We got pizza for the party. The weather was cold.

   _____

4. Dee makes her own pizza sauce. She buys crust.

   _____

5. Pizza has a lot of fat calories. It sure is good.

   _____

6. My mom doesn't eat pizza. Neither does my dad.

   _____

7. Pizza is a popular food. The grocery store closed.

   _____

Statements and Questions

A **statement** is a sentence that tells something.
A statement ends with a period. (.)

> The rainstorm flooded our backyard.

A **question** is a sentence that asks something.
A question ends with a question mark. (?)

> Did your yard flood, too**?**

Decide whether each sentence below is a statement or a question. Add a period if the sentence is a statement. Add a question mark if the sentence is a question.

1. We heard thunder while we were eating _____

2. Mom ran to call our dog, Koko _____

3. Koko did not come _____

4. Where did Koko go _____

5. Was she hiding in the garage _____

6. Was she playing with the neighbor's dog _____

7. Suddenly we heard Koko's loud barking _____

8. My brother laughed and ran upstairs _____

9. Someone had shut Koko in a bedroom by mistake _____

10. Will she ever trust us again _____

Exclamations and Commands

An **exclamation** is a sentence that shows strong feeling.
An exclamation ends with an exclamation point. (!)

What a terrific horror movie that was!

A **command** is a sentence that tells someone what to do.
A command ends with a period. (.)

Come to the movie with me.

Decide whether each sentence is an exclamation or a command. Write each sentence correctly.

1. don't give away the ending to the movie

_____

2. yikes, it's an alien

_____

3. wow, I was really scared

_____

4. tell your friend what time the movie starts

_____

5. pay for the popcorn at the food stand

_____

6. oh, gross, there's gum on my shoe

_____

7. cover your eyes at the scary parts

_____

©1999 School Zone Publishing Company

Context Clues

Sometimes the **context**, the words in a sentence or surrounding sentences, will help you understand a word you don't know.

The Milky Way galaxy is only one of many giant groups of stars.

If you don't know what *galaxy* means, you can figure out from the other words in the sentence that a galaxy is a giant group of stars.

Circle the word or words that help you figure out the meaning of the underlined word or phrase. Then write the meaning.

1. I like looking at the <u>constellations</u> on a clear night. These star patterns have strange and interesting shapes.

_____

2. They begin to show at <u>dusk</u>, just after sunset.

_____

3. I really like the constellation of The <u>Archer</u>. I can almost see him shooting his bow and arrow.

_____

4. Sometimes the stars seem to <u>shimmer</u>. It's as if they're on a switch that makes them brighter and dimmer.

_____

5. The stars are an <u>incredible</u> distance away. It really is unbelievable how far from Earth they are.

_____

6. Our <u>solar system</u> includes Earth, eight other planets, and the sun.

_____

©1999 School Zone Publishing Company

Write a Book Report

When you write a book report, tell the important events, or **plot**, of the book. But don't give away the ending. Explain the most important idea. Write about the main **characters**, the people or animals in the book, and the **setting**, where and when the story takes place. Finally, give your opinion of the book or explain why someone might or might not like to read it.

Read this book report about the book *Charlotte's Web*.

> Charlotte's Web by E.B. White tells the story of a pig named Wilbur and how his life is changed by a spider named Charlotte.
>
> The two animals live in a farmyard where they become friends. One day Wilbur hears that he will soon be killed for food. Charlotte says that she will save him and makes a clever plan. Learn whether her plan works in this book.
>
> You'll never forget Wilbur and Charlotte. They show what true friends are like. There are other great characters, too, including a funny goose and a sneaky rat. This book is loaded with information about animals. Did you know that a spider can spin a complete web every day? Some parts of Charlotte's Web are sad, but I encourage everyone to read this wonderful book.

1. What is this book about?

2. Circle the paragraph that tells about the plot.

3. Write two things the book report writer likes about *Charlotte's Web*.

_____

_____

_____

_____

©1999 School Zone Publishing Company

Plan Your Book Report

Choose a book you would like to share with other people.
Plan your book report here.

Title: _____

Author: _____

Main characters: _____

_____

Setting: _____

Plot: What are the most important events?

_____

_____

_____

_____

Most important idea: What does the author want you to understand after
you read this book?

_____

_____

Opinion: Your opinion is what you think or feel about the book. Are you glad
you read the book or not? Would you suggest that other people read it?

_____

_____

©1999 School Zone Publishing Company

Draft Your Book Report

Reread the report on *Charlotte's Web* on page 8. Then reread your notes about the book you read. Now, write your report. Use capital letters for the important words in the title of your book. Use capital letters for the author's name and the names of characters or special places.

Be sure to
☐ use capital letters in the title and author's name
☐ tell about the plot and main idea
☐ tell whether you recommend the book

Title: _____

Author: _____

_____

_____

_____

_____

_____

_____

_____

_____

_____

_____

©1999 School Zone Publishing Company

Revise Your Book Report

Read these examples. What is wrong? Use marks from the box to help you remember what to fix and how to fix it. Then write the examples correctly.

Title: James and the giant peach

_____

Author: roald Dahl

_____

Cross out the sentences that do not give an opinion or reasons for an opinion. Use the ⌀.

> I did not like this book. Most of the characters were silly. I did like the character Ally, because she was funny. I read another book by the same author once. The setting in this book was boring. Do all alien planets really look the same? The plot could have been more dramatic or scary. I had to stop reading because it was time for soccer practice.

Revise your book report. Then check your book report.

Did you write the title using capital letters?   yes   no

Did you write the author's name correctly?   yes   no

Did you write about the characters?   yes   no

Did you write about the setting and the plot?   yes   no

Did you write your opinion of the book?   yes   no

Fix sentences that do not begin with capital letters and end with punctuation marks. Take out words or sentences that stray from the topic or do not make sense. Use the proofreader's marks to help you.

Publish Your Book Report

When you publish your writing, you share it with others. First make a final copy of your writing. Then choose one way to share it.

Write the final copy of your book report here.

Title: _____

Author: _____

Choose a way to share your writing.

☐ Read your book report to your family.
☐ Give copies to friends to read.
☐ E-mail a copy.
☐ Work with friends to collect your reports in a book.

_____

_____

_____

_____

_____

_____

_____

_____

_____

_____

©1999 School Zone Publishing Company

What Is a Noun?

A **noun** is a word that names a person, place, animal, or thing.

We are going to visit my **aunt**.   (person)
She lives in a **forest**.   (place)
She studies the **wolf**.   (animal)
She wrote a **book**.   (thing)

Underline the nouns in the sentences. Then write each noun in the proper column.

1. We went skiing out west.

2. I fell and broke my arm.

3. My brother took me to the hospital.

4. At the hospital, the doctor put on a cast.

5. I was glad to get home.

6. I played quietly with our dog.

7. My uncle asked if I wanted new skis.

8. I said I'd rather have a bike.

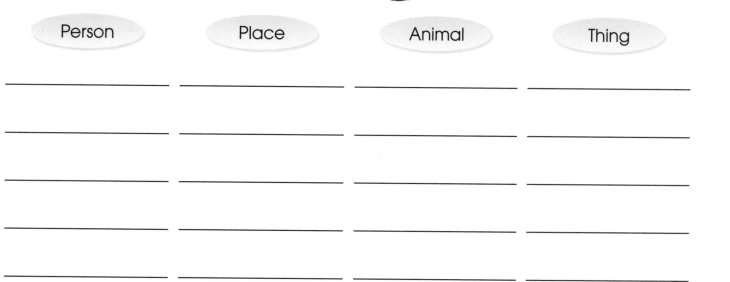

Person	Place	Animal	Thing
_____	_____	_____	_____
_____	_____	_____	_____
_____	_____	_____	_____
_____	_____	_____	_____
_____	_____	_____	_____

©1999 School Zone Publishing Company

Singular and Plural Nouns

A **singular noun** names one person, place, animal, or thing. A **plural noun** names more than one person, place, animal, or thing. Many plural nouns are formed by adding *s* to the singular noun.

> There is an apple **tree** outside my window.
> There are lots of apple **trees** in the park.

Write the plurals of the nouns under the blanks to complete the sentences.

1. I watched the _____ unload at the store.
   truck

2. The _____ carried in lots of _____ .
   guy   crate

3. One was full of _____ .
   banana

4. The _____ put them out for the _____ .
   clerk   customer

5. Someone unloaded _____ and _____ .
   apple   orange

6. I kept waiting for the _____ .
   lemon

7. I love lemon _____ and _____ .
   pie   cake

8. Oh, I almost forgot to watch for _____ !
   grape

9. I bought some fruit with my five _____ .
   dollar

10. I ate an apple and two _____ .
    pear

©1999 School Zone Publishing Company

Plural Nouns with *es*

Some nouns have special endings. These are *s*, *ss*, *x*, *sh*, and *ch*. The **plurals** for these nouns are formed by adding *es*.

dish ⟶ dish**es**
crash ⟶ crash**es**

Some nouns end in a consonant followed by *y*. To form the plurals for these nouns, change the *y* to *i* and add *es*.

city ⟶ cit**ies**

Finish the sentences by writing the plurals of the nouns under the blanks.

1. Two _____ took the four third-grade _____

bus class
   to the park.

2. Mrs. Miller brought _____ of _____ .

box lunch

3. We took _____ and _____ , too.

dish glass

4. We sang and told _____ on the bus.

story

5. At the park I saw some _____ on low _____

butterfly branch

   and two _____ near a tree.

bunny

 ©1999 School Zone Publishing Company

Proper Nouns

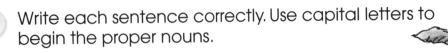

Proper nouns name particular people, places, animals, or things. Proper nouns begin with capital letters.

Name: Benito
Title: Mayor Ramsey
Place: Big Bend National Park

Write each sentence correctly. Use capital letters to begin the proper nouns.

1. miss sampson asked about our summer vacations.

_____

2. teddy and barb showed pictures of the everglades.

_____

3. The tafts liked florida better than texas.

_____

4. leroy saw wolves at yellowstone park.

_____

5. eli and the cohens went canoeing in michigan.

_____

6. roger's dad, doctor madison, helped a sick camper.

_____

7. randy and maria loved the grand canyon.

_____

8. The gurwitzes just escaped hurricane george.

_____

16

©1999 School Zone Publishing Company

Days, Months, and Holidays

new year's day
april
monday
weekend
fourth of july
halloween
birthday
summer
thursday
thanksgiving

Days, months, and holidays are proper nouns.

Monday
September
Passover

Write a day, month, or holiday from the word box to match each description. Capitalize the proper nouns.

1. day after Wednesday _____

2. spooky holiday _____

3. season with no school _____

4. first weekday of school _____

5. holiday for starting over _____

6. day you were born _____

7. two days at end of week _____

8. holiday for the United States _____

9. fourth month of the year _____

10. holiday with pumpkin pie _____

Initials and Abbreviations

An **initial** is the first letter in the name of a person or place. Initials are capital letters and are followed by periods.

James Louis Potter ⟶ J. L. Potter ⟶ J. L. P.

An **abbreviation** is a shortened form of a word. Abbreviations begin with capital letters. They end with periods.

Doctor Jones ⟶ **Dr.** Jones   Elm Street ⟶ Elm **St.**

Write the underlined abbreviations or initials in each sentence correctly.

1. <u>dr</u> Roberts has an office on Dunham <u>st</u>

_____

2. Tim Jones, <u>jr</u>, won the relay held at <u>tl</u> Wiley School.

_____

3. <u>mr</u> Ramirez and <u>ms</u> Rosario both live on Harper <u>ave</u>

_____

4. <u>gp</u> Bailey and Sons built the school on Belvoir <u>blvd</u>

_____

5. <u>gen</u> Homer Watkins lives with <u>mrs</u> Watkins.

_____

6. <u>mr</u> and <u>mrs</u> Bell live on Oak <u>st</u> near Bay <u>ct</u>

_____

Possessive Nouns

A **possessive noun** shows ownership. Add an apostrophe (')
and *s* to most singular nouns to make them possessive.

> Jake**'s** backpack was lost in the flood.

Add an apostrophe after *s* in plural nouns to make them possessive.

> The boy**s'** backpacks were lost in the flood.

Write the possessive nouns in the sentences correctly.

1. The kangaroos family is called marsupials. _____

2. The smallest marsupial is a rabbits size! _____

3. Kangaroos powerful hind legs help them move quickly. _____

4. These marsupials strong tails are used for balance. _____

5. A baby kangaroo lives in the mothers pouch at first. _____

6. Most other mammals babies do not have a pouch. _____

7. A kangaroo babys early life is warm and cozy. _____

8. The kangaroo is one of Australias best-known marsupials. _____

©1999 School Zone Publishing Company

Homographs

Homographs are words that are spelled the same but have different meanings. Some homographs are also pronounced differently.

Our savings **bank** is on the **bank** of the Fox River.

The first meaning of *bank* is a place you put your money. The second meaning is the land alongside a river.

Circle the letter of the definition of each homograph.

1. My friend Jack is at <u>bat</u>.
   a. small flying animal   b. take a turn at trying to hit a ball

2. I hope he breaks his home run <u>record</u>.
   a. do something better than ever before   b. put music on tape or CD

3. Is it a <u>fly</u> ball?
   a. insect with two wings   b. baseball hit high in the air

4. No, it's out of the <u>park</u>!
   a. area of land   b. leave a car in a garage or at the curb

Write the meaning of the homographs.

5. Let's buy the top on the top shelf.

_____

6. I long for thick, long hair.

_____

7. Our dog leaves fall leaves all over the house.

_____

8. Please watch my watch while I'm swimming.

_____

©1999 School Zone Publishing Company

Outlines

Writers use outlines to organize information for reports, articles, and other kinds of writing. The **title** of an outline gives the topic. The **main topics** are listed after Roman numerals and periods. The **subtopics**, or details about the main topics, follow capital letters and periods. Subtopics are indented.

Title: Two Ancient Reptiles

Main Topic: I. Alligator
                      A. Where it lives
Subtopics: B. Characteristics
                      C. Family life

Main Topic: II. Crocodile
                      A. Where it lives
Subtopics: B. Characteristics
                      C. Family life

Write A., B., or C. after the phrases about alligators to show where they would fit on the outline.

1. Female lays 50 eggs _____   2. Grows to 12 feet _____

3. Southern U.S. _____   4. Has rounded snout _____

5. Babies stay with mother _____ 6. China _____

If you wanted to enter the following information about the crocodile, under which heading would each phrase go?

7. Pointed snout _____   8. Mostly in tropical countries _____

9. Grows to 21 feet _____   10. Babies hatch at 3-1/2 months _____

Main and Helping Verbs

A **main verb** is the most important verb in the predicate. A **helping verb** works with the main verb. Some helping verbs are forms of the verb *have*.

Jody **has run** relays in track meets many times.

The helping verb *has* works with the main verb *run* to describe the action.

Write the correct helping verb in the blank to complete each sentence.

1. Jody _____ trained to be an Olympic runner.
    (has, had, have)

2. By the time she was eight, she _____ run in several local races.
    (has, had, have)

3. Her brother Randy _____ given her some good training tips.
    (has, had, have)

4. She _____ lost some races, and Randy tells her that's OK.
    (has, had, have)

5. He also tells her that she _____ to improve her speed.
    (has, had, have)

6. Jody and Randy _____ run a race together.
    (has, had, have)

7. Jody's muscles _____ loosened since she started stretching them
    (has, had, have)
    more often.

8. We all _____ watched Jody run in races.
    (has, had, have)

Present and Past Tense

The **tense** of a verb tells when the action of a verb takes place. The **present tense** tells what is happening now or what happens regularly.

> Our dog chews through a boot in two minutes.
> The neighbor's dogs chew boots, too.

The **past tense** tells what already happened. Many verbs form their past tense by adding *ed*.

> Clancy chewed my brother's notebook last night.

Write *present* or *past* to describe the tense of the underlined verb in each sentence.

1. I <u>wash</u> my dog, Clancy, about once a month. _____

2. He usually <u>likes</u> his bath. _____

3. Sometimes he <u>barks</u> when he doesn't want a bath. _____

4. Last week he <u>dashed</u> away from me before I could catch him. _____

5. But I <u>dished</u> up some food to try to bring him back. _____

6. He always <u>trots</u> back home when he smells his food. _____

7. After I put the food down, I <u>waited</u> to grab him. _____

8. After his bath, I <u>combed</u> him dry. _____

23

©1999 School Zone Publishing Company

The Verb *Be*

The verb *be* tells what something is or was. *Be* joins the subject to the predicate. Below are the present and past tenses of *be*.

Present: I *am* happy on the ice.
My sister *is* in the warming hut.
Her friends *are* roasting marshmallows.

Past: Last year, I *was* scared of falling.
Ice and snow *were* new to me.

Write *present* or *past* after each sentence.

1. My skates <u>are</u> really perfect. _____

2. They <u>were</u> a present from Aunt Tilda. _____

3. I <u>was</u> sure I would like living where it snows. _____

4. My brother and sister <u>were</u> not as certain. _____

5. I <u>am</u> excited when I see dark clouds. _____

6. That means snow <u>is</u> about to fall. _____

7. The ice <u>is</u> frozen most of the winter. _____

8. I <u>am</u> ready to skate after school any day. _____

9. But homework and chores <u>are</u> ready for me. _____

10. Oh well, my skates <u>are</u> ready when I <u>am</u>. _____

©1999 School Zone Publishing Company

Future Tense

The **future tense** of a verb tells what will happen tomorrow, next month, or any time to come. The future tense adds the helping verb *will* to the main verb.

Present: I **watch** the stars on a clear night.
Past: Last night I **watched** the Big Dipper.
Future: Tomorrow I **will watch** the full moon.

Rewrite each sentence using the future tense of the underlined verb.

1. Our class <u>started</u> a school garden.

_____

2. We <u>spend</u> time in our garden each week.

_____

3. We think the flowers <u>make</u> the schoolyard pretty.

_____

4. We also <u>grow</u> vegetables in the garden.

_____

5. We <u>give</u> some vegetables to feed hungry people.

_____

6. Suni <u>plants</u> beans.

_____

7. I <u>pick</u> peas, and Grant <u>digs</u> carrots.

_____

8. We all <u>weed</u> the garden regularly.

_____

 ©1999 School Zone Publishing Company

Irregular Verbs

Irregular verbs do not end with *ed* to show the past tense. Here are some irregular verbs.

Present	Past	Present	Past
come	came	go	went
do	did	run	ran
eat	ate	see	saw

Complete each sentence by writing the correct tense.

1. We _____ to the neighborhood street fair on Sunday.
   (go, past)

2. Lots of people from around the city _____ to the fair each year.
   (come, present)

3. There is always lots to _____ and _____ .
   (see, present)   *(do, present)*

4. Last year we _____ a relay to help raise money for a child care center.
   (run, past)

5. Then we _____ corn dogs until our parents _____ to get us.
   (eat, past)   *(come, past)*

6. Often we _____ early to see the magic show.
   (go, present)

7. Once we _____ in just in time to see the magician disappear.
   (come, past)

8. On Sunday we _____ too much and _____ too much and
   (eat, past)   *(do, past)*
   got very tired.

9. Usually, when we get home, we don't _____ for days.
   (eat, present)

10. Our parents, who _____ with us one year, slept until ten the next day.
    (come, past)

                    ©1999 School Zone Publishing Company

Write a Persuasive Paragraph

When you write to persuade, you try to convince your readers to believe what you believe or to take action about something. Newspaper editorials and letters to the editor are examples of persuasive writing.

In a persuasive paragraph, you first write a **topic sentence** that explains what your paragraph is about. Then you write some **reasons** you hold your opinion. Finally, you may **restate** your feelings and ask readers to agree with you or to do something.

Read this persuasive paragraph.

Building a new office building at the corner of Elm St. and Superior St. would be a terrible mistake! This office building and its parking lot would ruin the park that's between Superior and Terrace. There are many beautiful old trees that would be cut down. These trees and green space are homes for birds and animals. The park is a place for walking, running, playing ball, and learning about nature. Last week our class studied water life in the creek in the park. There are other places to put office buildings, but there are very few park areas left. Please come to the City Council meeting next week and speak up to save the park!

1. About what does the writer have a strong opinion?

_____

2. What does the writer think the office building will do?

_____

3. Why does the writer think the park should be saved?

_____

_____

4. What does the writer want readers to do?

_____

Plan Your Persuasive Paragraph

Think of something about which you have strong feelings or a strong opinion. Perhaps you want the school lunchroom to have more healthful meals. Maybe you love animals and want to tell people to take better care of their pets. Or perhaps you like someone who is running for office and want to tell readers why.

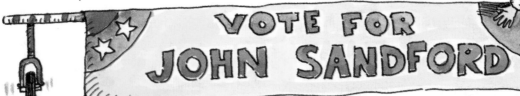

Plan your persuasive paragraph here.

Topic: _____

Opinions and feelings about the topic:

_____

_____

_____

Reasons and/or facts to back up your opinion:

_____

_____

_____

What should readers do or believe?

_____

_____

_____

Draft Your Persuasive Paragraph

Reread the paragraph about the park on page 27. Notice that the writer uses words that signal opinions, such as "I think" and "I believe." The writer states her opinion clearly. She doesn't want to see an office building go up, and she gives several reasons why.

Reread the paragraph about the park on page 27.

Be sure to
- [ ] use capital letters to begin sentences and the names of people and places
- [ ] write complete sentences
- [ ] give your opinion and back it up
- [ ] suggest what readers can do if they share your opinion

Write a draft of your persuasive paragraph.

_____

_____

_____

_____

_____

_____

_____

_____

_____

_____

Revise Your Persuasive Paragraph

Read these examples. What is missing? Use marks from the box to show corrections. Then write the examples correctly.

Proofreader's Marks
≡ Capital letter
⊙ Add period
✀ Take out
∧ Put in

I believe jan parker should be elected student council president. She listens to everybody and has good leadership qualities. Who could do a better job

_____

_____

Look at these sentences. Take out the sentences that do not state an opinion or give reasons for an opinion. Use the ✀ from the box.

I think Adele Smith deserves the Athlete of the Year award. She runs and swims. She plays soccer and basketball. She lives on our street. She keeps her grades up, too. I feel she is the best athlete this school has ever had. Please vote for her! The next soccer game is Friday.

Revise your persuasive paragraph. Then check your paragraph.

Did you use capital letters to begin sentences?	yes	no
Did you use capital letters for proper names?	yes	no
Did you state your opinion clearly?	yes	no
Did you use phrases such as "I believe"?	yes	no
Did you give reasons for your opinion?	yes	no
Did you ask readers to take some action?	yes	no

Fix sentences that do not begin with capital letters and end with end marks. Take out words or sentences that do not add to the meaning. Use proofreader's marks to help you.

Publish Your Persuasive Paragraph

When you publish your writing, share it with others. First make a final copy of your writing. Then choose one way to share it.

Write the final copy of your persuasive paragraph here.

_____

_____

_____

_____

_____

_____

_____

_____

_____

_____

_____

_____

_____

Choose a way to share your writing.

☐ If your opinion is about something at school, send your paragraph in letter form to the editor of the school newspaper.

☐ If your opinion is about something in the community, send it to the editor of the community newspaper.

☐ If your opinion is about something important to your classmates, read it to them and ask for other examples of persuasive writing on the same subject.

©1999 School Zone Publishing Company

What Is a Pronoun?

A **pronoun** is a word that takes the place of a noun.

> **Jamie** knows all about snakes. **He** knows all about snakes.

He takes the place of *Jamie*.

Singular pronouns: *I, me, you, he, she, him, her, it*
Plural pronouns: *we, us, they, them, you*

Underline the pronouns.

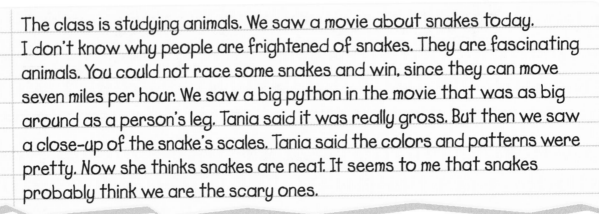

The class is studying animals. We saw a movie about snakes today.
I don't know why people are frightened of snakes. They are fascinating
animals. You could not race some snakes and win, since they can move
seven miles per hour. We saw a big python in the movie that was as big
around as a person's leg. Tania said it was really gross. But then we saw
a close-up of the snake's scales. Tania said the colors and patterns were
pretty. Now she thinks snakes are neat. It seems to me that snakes
probably think we are the scary ones.

Write two or three sentences about snakes. Include some pronouns.

_____

_____

_____

_____

_____

_____

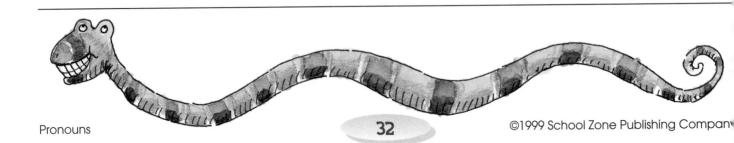

©1999 School Zone Publishing Company

Subject Pronouns

A **subject pronoun** takes the place of a noun or nouns in the subject of a sentence.

The oldest son plays the trumpet. **He** plays it very loud. *He* takes the place of *the oldest son*.

Some subject pronouns: *he, she, it, you, we, they*

Write a pronoun in each blank to replace the underlined word or words.

<u>Ramon</u> was excited because _____ was going to play in the band at a

football game for the first time. He polished his trumpet until <u>the trumpet</u> _____

shined. Then he blew a few notes to see how <u>the notes</u> _____ sounded.

Ramon's friend Rosa came to practice with him. <u>Rosa</u> _____ plays the

clarinet. The two players practiced the school fight song. They did not like the way <u>the</u>

<u>school fight song</u> _____ sounded. So they practiced over and over. Finally

<u>Rosa and Ramon</u> _____ were satisfied.

Rosa said <u>Rosa</u> _____ would meet Ramon at the band bus. Ramon said

<u>Ramon</u> _____ would be there. The two kids hoped their parents would come

to the game. <u>Their parents</u> _____ particularly like to hear the trumpet and

clarinet.

Object Pronouns

An **object pronoun** takes the place of a noun or nouns in the predicate of a sentence.

Some object pronouns: *me, you, him, her, it, us, them*

> Max watched **the shark video**. Max enjoyed **it**.

It takes the place of *the shark video*.

Write an object pronoun to complete each rhyme.

1. This belongs to Joe and Clem.

   Yes, I'll give the book to _____ .

2. Look, did Marcy get a hit?

   Wow, she really blasted _____ !

3. The spotted dog ran up to Jim.

   Every day it waits for _____ .

4. I brought some cookies and some tea.

   So come and have some lunch with _____ .

5. Your shoes are pretty. Are they new?

   They look so very fine on _____ .

6. Lashanda sleeps and doesn't stir.

   We'll try not to awaken _____ .

7. Leroy's jacket doesn't fit.

   Perhaps now he'll get rid of _____ .

 ©1999 School Zone Publishing Compan

I and Me

I is a subject pronoun that takes the place of your name.
Me is an object pronoun that takes the place of your name.
When you write about another person and yourself, always
name yourself last.

Mom and I picked out our new computer.
Mom taught **me** to use the computer.

Write *I* or *me* to complete each sentence.

1. _____ thought using a computer would be hard.

2. It took _____ three hours to learn to work the VCR.

3. But mom made the computer easy for _____ .

4. First, _____ learned how to get into a word program.

5. Then she taught _____ how to write things and move them around.

6. It was hard for _____ to learn how to save our work.

7. A letter to my grandmother disappeared before _____ caught on.

8. Now _____ wonder how anybody works without a computer.

9. My mom says she will teach _____ how to work with pictures on the screen.

10. _____ am lucky to have a techie mom!

Possessive Pronouns

A **possessive pronoun** shows ownership. Some possessive pronouns take the place of nouns. These are *my, your, his, her, its, our, your,* and *their*.

> These are **my** skates. Those are **your** boots.

Other possessive pronouns can stand alone. These are *mine, yours, his, hers, ours, yours,* and *theirs*.

> These are my skates. These skates are **mine**.
> That is your magic marker. That magic marker is **yours**.

Underline the possessive pronouns.

1. If I were a detective, I could use my magnifying glass.

2. I could catch a jewel thief doing his evil deeds.

3. I would track thieves by their fingerprints.

4. What if I found fingerprints that were not theirs?

5. Then I would ask my trusted assistant for her help.

6. Together we would solve our case.

7. No detective agency would be better than ours!

8. We might discover a secret plot to kidnap a general and his family.

9. Of course, not all the glory would be mine.

10. Some would be hers.

©1999 School Zone Publishing Company

Direct Quotes

A direct quote shows the exact words someone says.
Quotation marks (" ") come before and after the speaker's
words. A comma, question mark, or exclamation point
comes after the speaker's exact words and before the
rest of the sentence.

"We're going through an asteroid path," said the captain.
"There's one now," cried the first officer. "Look out!"

Add quotation marks to the sentences.

1. Go to warp speed! shouted the captain.

2. I can't, answered the first officer. Our warp engines are down.

3. Does anybody have any ideas? asked the captain.

4. The engineer replied, We could reverse the engines to push the ship backward.

5. Try it! ordered the captain. We have to try everything!

6. It's working! yelled the first officer.

7. We're going backward, but the asteroid is still too close, she added.

8. Suddenly the engineer cried, The warp engines are back up. Let's get out of here!

9. Please steer clear of asteroids for a while, sighed the captain. That's an order!

0. Is anybody hungry? asked the cook. It's time for lunch.

37

©1999 School Zone Publishing Company

Using Quotation Marks for Titles

Use quotation marks when you write the titles of stories, poems, songs, or articles.

I love Springsteen's "Born in the USA."
My young sister likes "Hakuna Matata" from *The Lion King*.

Place quotation marks correctly in the sentences below.

1. Did you read the editorial Why Vote? in today's paper?

2. Yes, and I liked the letter to the editor entitled The Responsibilities of a Citizen.

3. I think Candle in the Wind is a very sad song.

4. But the article The Death of a Princess was much sadder.

5. I've always loved Rocky Mountain High by John Denver.

6. I prefer Take Me Home, Country Roads myself.

7. The poem Steam Shovel compares the machine to a dinosaur.

8. Yes, and the poem Garden Hose compares the hose to a snake.

9. There's a piece in the paper today called Save the Park.

10. That's because last week someone wrote Build the Mall.

11. Is The Telltale Heart one of Edgar Allen Poe's short stories?

12. Yes, but Jack London wrote To Build a Fire.

Write a note to a friend telling about your current favorite songs or a good story you have read recently.

_____

_____

_____

38

©1999 School Zone Publishing Company

What Is an Adjective?

An **adjective** is a word that describes a noun.

Luke is reading about **ancient** animals.
These **fascinating** creatures are now **extinct**.

Circle the adjectives that describe the underlined nouns.

1. The word *dinosaur* means "terrible <u>lizard</u>."

2. Dinosaurs were probably the biggest <u>animals</u> that ever lived on land.

3. These huge <u>dinosaurs</u> were excellent <u>walkers</u>.

4. Their thundering <u>footsteps</u> could probably be heard over a large <u>area</u>.

5. The smaller <u>animals</u> could run fast.

6. One kind of adult <u>dinosaur</u> was the size of a chicken!

7. Young <u>dinosaurs</u> stayed in muddy <u>nests</u>.

8. Dinosaurs had sharp <u>eyesight</u> and keen <u>hearing</u>.

9. Some dinosaurs ate huge, leafy <u>ferns</u>.

10. Both meat <u>eaters</u> and plant <u>eaters</u> lived when Earth had a warmer <u>climate</u>.

11. Scientists do not know if <u>dinosaurs</u> were gray or green.

12. Perhaps a cooler <u>climate</u> caused dinosaurs to die out.

13. Maybe a plunging <u>asteroid</u> helped them along.

14. Some <u>scientists</u> believe that yesterday's <u>dinosaur</u> is related to today's <u>bird</u>.

15. New <u>facts</u> about these amazing <u>animals</u> appear regularly.

Write a sentence about dinosaurs that includes one or more adjectives.

_____

©1999 School Zone Publishing Company

Adjectives That Tell How Many and What Kind

Some adjectives tell how many or what kind.

> We won **three** tickets to a **magic** show.

The word *three* tells how many. *Magic* tells what kind.

Circle the adjectives that describe the underlined nouns.

1. The tall <u>magician</u> was dressed in a white <u>coat</u>.

2. First, he raised his long, black <u>wand</u>.

3. Then he made several red <u>scarves</u> appear from his sleeve!

4. Next he spoke a few magic <u>words</u> and the scarves disappeared!

5. Would he do the famous <u>trick</u> with the two locked <u>cabinets</u>?

6. No, instead he wrapped many heavy <u>chains</u> around him.

7. Then his two <u>assistants</u> dropped him into a huge water <u>tank</u>!

8. Of course he got loose in one <u>minute</u>.

9. Then he took a grand <u>bow</u>.

Write adjectives that tell how many or what kind to complete each sentence.

10. I saw _____ squirrels and _____ robins in the park last week.

11. The squirrels were eating and burying _____ nuts.

12. A _____ dog ran after the squirrels.

13. They scurried into the _____ trees and chattered.

14. Suddenly, _____ gulls soared over the _____ lake.

15. I had _____ hours of _____ homework to do, so I headed hom

Articles

A, *an*, and *the* are called **articles**.

A and *an* refer to any person, place, animal, or thing.

A is used before nouns that begin with consonant sounds.

> Let's have **a** party!

An is used before nouns that begin with vowel sounds.

> That's **an** awesome idea!

The refers to a specific person, place, animal, or thing.

> **The** party will be at my house. You bring **the** games.

Write the correct article in each sentence.

1. I've never planned _____ party before.
   (a, an)

2. I have _____ idea that I think _____ guests will like.
   (a, an)   (the, an)

3. We'll have _____ party at _____ roller rink.
   (an, the)   (a, an)

4. Everyone will get _____ invitation soon.
   (an, the)

5. Should we have _____ regular cake or _____ ice-cream cake?
   (a, the)   (a, an)

6. Or should we just order _____ huge pizza with everything?
   (a, an)

7. Let's all chip in for _____ gift for Joe.
   (an, the)

8. I know he'd like _____ astronomy T-shirt with Earth and all
   (a, an)
   _____ planets on it.
   (a, the)

©1999 School Zone Publishing Company

Adjectives That Compare

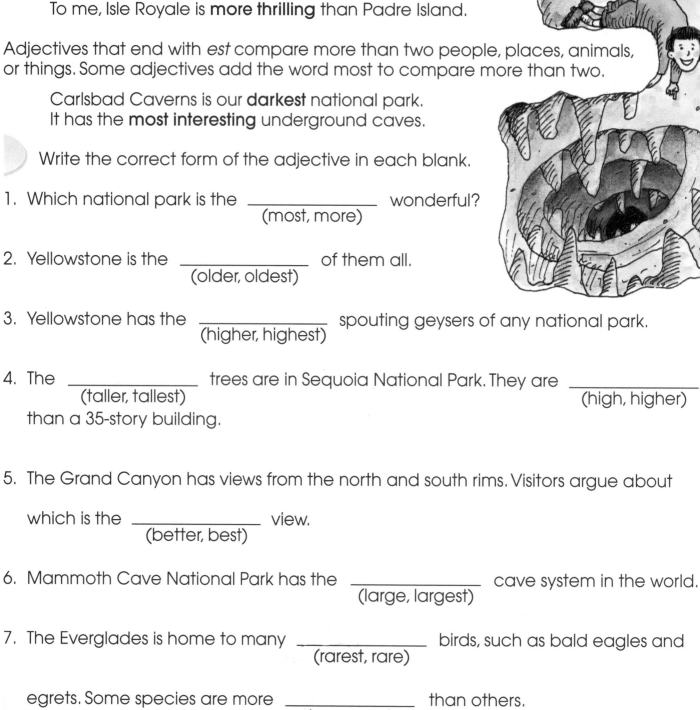

Adjectives that end with *er* compare two people, places, animals, or things. Some adjectives add the word *more* to compare two.

> Padre Island is **bigger** than many other national seashores.
> To me, Isle Royale is **more thrilling** than Padre Island.

Adjectives that end with *est* compare more than two people, places, animals, or things. Some adjectives add the word most to compare more than two.

> Carlsbad Caverns is our **darkest** national park.
> It has the **most interesting** underground caves.

Write the correct form of the adjective in each blank.

1. Which national park is the _____ wonderful?
   (most, more)

2. Yellowstone is the _____ of them all.
   (older, oldest)

3. Yellowstone has the _____ spouting geysers of any national park.
   (higher, highest)

4. The _____ trees are in Sequoia National Park. They are _____
   (taller, tallest)   (high, higher)
   than a 35-story building.

5. The Grand Canyon has views from the north and south rims. Visitors argue about

   which is the _____ view.
   (better, best)

6. Mammoth Cave National Park has the _____ cave system in the world.
   (large, largest)

7. The Everglades is home to many _____ birds, such as bald eagles and
   (rarest, rare)

   egrets. Some species are more _____ than others.
   (rare, rarer)

8. I think the _____ animal of the Everglades is a bird called the anhinga.
   (stranger, strangest)

 ©1999 School Zone Publishing Company

Write a Story

Characters are the people or animals in a story. Most stories have a **setting**, where and when the story takes place. A story has a **plot**, what happens in the story.

The beginning of a story introduces the main character or characters and describes a problem they have. The beginning usually describes the setting. The middle of the story tells what the characters do to solve the problem. The end of the story tells how the characters do (or do not) solve the problem.

Read this short story.

Shelter in a Storm

I didn't expect to be a hero that weekend last year. It just happened. When the sudden snowstorm blew out of the mountains, we knew our plans for camping were lost.

"Whew, I can hardly see," gasped Jerry, as we struggled up the mountain. "Where did you say that cabin was, Andy?"

"I don't remember exactly," I yelled, my heart beating fast. "I was only there once."

"We have to keep going," shouted Ashley over the howling wind.

We plodded on, our legs and feet growing heavier and heavier. I tried to keep a picture of the cabin in my mind. My family hiked there on a clear day. Today we couldn't see more than a few inches in front of us.

"Andy, do you see anything familiar?" asked Ashley, shivering. "I don't think I can go on much longer."

"There," I shouted. "Come on guys, only a few more yards." We fell through the cabin door and hurried to light a fire. Then we took off our cold outer clothing and wrapped ourselves in blankets. The cabin was stocked with dry food, so we wouldn't starve. We would just wait out the storm.

1. Who are the characters?

_____

2. What is the setting?

_____

3. What is the plot?

_____

_____

 ©1999 School Zone Publishing Company

Plan Your Story

What should your story be about? What have you done lately that could be part of a story? Have you read any articles or books that gave you story ideas?

Write some ideas below.

Story Ideas:

_____

_____

_____

Choose one of your ideas. Now plan your story.

Setting: _____

_____

Main Character(s): _____

_____

_____

Plot: What happens to the characters in the story? What are the main events? How does one event cause another one?

_____

_____

_____

©1999 School Zone Publishing Company

Draft Your Story

Reread the short story on page 43. Then reread your notes about the story you are writing.

Now you are ready to write your first draft.

Remember to
- ☐ introduce the characters
- ☐ describe the setting
- ☐ include a plot with a beginning, middle, and end
- ☐ put quotation marks around characters' exact words

Title: _____

Author: _____

_____

_____

_____

_____

_____

_____

_____

_____

_____

_____

_____

_____

_____

_____

_____

_____

_____

Revise Your Story

Read this example. Use the proofreader's marks from the box to make corrections.

> "Throw it over here! yelled Marcia.
>   No, throw it here!" shouted tony. the two children were playing football with their father.
>   Suddenly mr. Vento tripped and fell. Ouch, he hollered. I think I broke my leg!

Proofreader's Marks

☰ Capital letter
⊙ Add period
⌐ Indent
∧ Put in

Revise your story.

Did you create a setting for your story?   yes   no

Did you introduce the characters and tell something about them?   yes   no

Does your story have a beginning, middle, and end?   yes   no

Add parts to your story that you forgot. Make other changes so that your story is just the way you want it.

Proofread your story.

Did you use capital letters to begin sentences and characters' names?   yes   no

Did you use quotation marks around the exact words characters said?   yes   no

Use proofreader's marks to make corrections.

Publish Your Story

Write the final copy of your short story. Use a second sheet of paper if you need to.

Choose a way to share your writing.
- [ ] Read your story to some friends or relatives.
- [ ] Give a copy of your story to someone.
- [ ] E-mail a copy to a relative or friend in another town or state.
- [ ] Combine efforts with some friends to produce a collection of your short stories.

_____

_____

_____

_____

_____

_____

_____

_____

_____

_____

_____

_____

_____

_____

©1999 School Zone Publishing Company

What Is an Adverb?

An **adverb** is a word that tells about, or **describes**, a verb. Adverbs can tell *when*, *where*, or *how*.

The cat will leap **soon**.	when
She will leap **down** on the dog.	where
The cat **carefully** plans her leaps.	how

Underline the adverbs in the sentences. On each blank, tell whether the adverb tells when, where, or how.

1. Our dog, Muffin, was snoring noisily. _____

2. The cat, Rami, eyed him cautiously. _____

3. Rami sometimes misjudged her leaps. _____

4. She might jump over Muffin. _____

5. Then he would wake suddenly and yawn. _____

6. If she leaped too close, he would bite her. _____

7. He bit playfully, so she wasn't afraid. _____

8. Still, Rami preferred to land near Muffin. _____

9. Then she would yowl loudly and wake him up. _____

10. Finally, they would chase madly after each other. _____

Write several sentences about something you and your family like to do together. Use adverbs that tell how, when, and where.

_____

_____

_____

_____

Adverbs   48   ©1999 School Zone Publishing Company

Adverbs That Tell How

Many adverbs tell *how* an action takes place. These adverbs usually end with *ly*. If a word ends in *y*, change the *y* to *i* and add *ly*.

The spy crept **secretly** into the fort.
Does anyone do homework **happily**?

In each blank, write the adverb form of the word in parentheses.

1. I will die (immediate) _____ if I climb that hill.

2. No, I think you just get tired (quick) _____ .

3. Well, I was (complete) _____ bushed after the hike.

4. Let's leave (prompt) _____ at 7:30 tomorrow.

5. We'll have to leave (quiet) _____ or we'll wake Mom.

6. She would be (extreme) _____ mad if we did that.

7. I can (easy) _____ leave the house by jumping out my window!

8. No, you'd be walking (painful) _____ all day.

Make adverbs from these adjectives.

9. icy _____

10. cool _____

11. impatient _____

12. slow _____

13. unhappy _____

14. safe _____

©1999 School Zone Publishing Company

Good and Well

Good is an adjective that tells what kind. When used after an action verb, *well* is an adverb that tells how. *Well* is an adjective when it is used after a linking verb such as *is, feels,* or *seems.*

> Alien is a **good** movie. It has a good cast. (adjective)
> The special effects are done **well**. (adverb)
> But I didn't feel very **well** after I saw it. (adjective)

Write adjective or adverb to identify each underlined word.

1. The new student is a <u>good</u> soccer player. _____

2. Yes, she played <u>well</u> in the tryouts. _____

3. We need a <u>good</u> goalie. _____

4. Yes, Angie is <u>good</u> but she has been ill. _____

5. I hope she will be <u>well</u> soon. _____

6. She didn't feel very <u>well</u> yesterday when I talked to her. _____

7. She said she was watching a <u>good</u> video. _____

8. But she definitely did not think her medicine was <u>good</u>! _____

9. How <u>well</u> do you think the team will do tonight? _____

10. We will all play as <u>well</u> as we can. _____

11. But will that be <u>good</u> enough? _____

12. I hope so, or I won't feel very <u>well</u>! _____

©1999 School Zone Publishing Company

Adverbs That Tell Where

Some adverbs tell where or in what direction.

Where did the cat go? She ran over **there**.

Underline the adverb in each sentence.

1. My dog, Frodo, hates to come inside on a nice day.

2. He runs down to the lake to hide.

3. I have looked everywhere for Frodo.

4. Once he stayed behind me so I would not see him.

5. Most days he runs far ahead of me.

6. I don't think he would ever run away.

7. But I worry about Frodo getting lost outside.

8. That's why I try to stay close to him.

9. Oh, there he goes up to the house.

10. If he wants to go inside, he must be hungry!

Write several sentences of your own. Include some of the adverbs you underlined in the sentences above.

_____

_____

_____

_____

_____

©1999 School Zone Publishing Company

Adverbs That Tell When

twice   soon
yesterday   later
before   already

Some adverbs tell when.

> We went to the rock concert **yesterday**.
> The group will also be performing **today**.

Use an adverb from the box to complete each rhyme.

1. Will we ever see the full moon?

   In the east, it will rise _____ .

2. Have you seen an alligator?

   Stick around, we'll see one _____ .

3. Have you seen my two pet mice?

   Yes, I did, I saw them _____ .

4. Have you heard from Dan and Jay?

   Yes, we saw them _____ .

5. I want to call my puppy Freddy,

   Look, he knows his name _____ .

6. Here's some cake, if you want more.

   Thanks, I'll drink some milk _____ .

©1999 School Zone Publishing Company

Adverbs That Compare

Adverbs that compare two actions end with *er*. Adverbs that compare three or more actions end with *est*.

The game started **late** last night.
The game last week started even **later**.
The homecoming game started **latest** of all.

Write the correct form of the adverb in parentheses to complete each group of sentences.

1. Many peaks rise _____ , but Mount Everest rises _____ than

   any mountain on the earth. It rises _____ of them all. (high)

2. My dog runs _____ than yours. You may think yours runs _____ ,

   but mine runs the _____ of any dog on our street. (fast)

3. Abdul plays _____ than any member of our team. I thought I played

   the _____ of anyone, but Abdul shows me that I only play

   _____ . (hard)

4. I grew _____ over the summer, but many of my friends grew even

   _____ . Sandy grew the _____ of all of us. (tall)

5. The Halloween party will start _____ . Last year it started the

   _____ of any year. If we get ready early, this year's party will start

   _____ than last year. (soon)

 ©1999 School Zone Publishing Company

Negative Words

No and *not* are negative words. *No* is often an adjective.

 I have **no** luck shopping for clothes.

Not is an adverb.

 I do **not** mind going to stores.

Some other negative words are *none, never, nothing, no one,* and *nobody*.

Write the negative word or words in each sentence.

1. Nothing I see comes in the right color. _____

2. Sometimes I do not like the fabric. _____

3. Often none of things I like are in my size. _____

4. Last week, nobody would wait on me. _____

5. No one else seems to have problems shopping. _____

6. Liu never comes home from shopping empty-handed. _____

7. There is nowhere she likes more than Bonn's. _____

8. None of my friends will shop for clothes with me. _____

9. Too bad there are no shopping classes! _____

10. But I guess that's not the solution. _____

54

©1999 School Zone Publishing Company

Adverbs or Adjectives?

An adverb tells about a verb. An adjective tells about a noun or pronoun.

The **tiny** puppy barked **constantly**.

The word *tiny* is an adjective that tells about the noun *puppy*. The word *constantly* tells when or how about the verb *barked*.

Circle the adjectives and underline the adverbs in the sentences.

1. The ideas for many common inventions may have come from animals.

2. The turtle has solid, armor plates for protection. Humans use tanks that move slowly and carry soldiers safely.

3. The rattlesnake shakes its loud rattle if an enemy walks nearby. People can protect their homes with noisy alarms to warn of burglars.

4. Birds carefully avoid the bright red ladybug, which contains poison. Red signals warn traffic to stop regularly.

5. Insects and birds fly easily by rapidly beating their wings. Air moves over a wing on an airplane and causes the wing to move upward.

6. Beavers have large, sharp teeth for cutting down trees. People use chisels to shape wood carefully.

7. Bats make high sounds that bounce against small insects. These echoes help bats locate food instantly. People use sonar, a sound system for locating objects underwater.

8. Ducks have soft, downy feathers which trap layers of warm air. Their young can sleep comfortably. People make special material in the same way for campers to wear outside.

Contractions

A **contraction** is a short way to write two words. The words are joined and a letter or letters are left out. An apostrophe (') takes the place of the left-out letter or letters.

I **do not** know his name.   I **don't** know his name.

Some common contractions with *not* are **aren't** (*are not*), **can't** (*can not*), **isn't** (*is not*), **doesn't** (*does not*), **don't** (*do not*), **shouldn't** (*should not*), **haven't** (*have not*), **hasn't** (*has not*), and **couldn't** (*could not*). The contraction **won't** is short for *will not*.

She **will not** be home.   She **won't** be home.

Write the contractions for the underlined words.

1. <u>Does not</u> _____ it seem that life is full of rules?

2. The traffic signs say <u>do not</u> _____ walk.

3. And we <u>should not</u> _____ dive into the deep end.

4. It <u>is not</u> _____ proper to talk with your mouth full.

5. In the woods, we <u>can not</u> _____ leave the path.

6. During the test, we <u>could not</u> _____ ask questions.

7. And we <u>will not</u> _____ watch TV before we study.

8. <u>Do not</u> _____ the rules ever change?

9. <u>Are not</u> _____ we old enough to make up our own?

10. Why <u>could not</u> _____ someone write some new ones?

11. Who <u>does not</u> _____ have some good ideas?

12. Why <u>have not</u> _____ we thought of this before?

     ©1999 School Zone Publishing Company

Conjunctions

A **conjunction** is a word that joins words, sentence parts, or sentences. Common conjunctions are *and*, *or*, and *but*. When you join two sentences together with conjunctions, use a comma before the conjunction.

I like to run, **but** I am too slow for the track team.
The best wrestler is Aaron, **and** everyone knows it.
The fastest swimmer is Katie, **or** maybe it's Mimi.

Write *and*, *or*, or *but* to connect each pair of sentences to make the most sense.

1. Should we go skating? Should we play catch?

_____

2. Ben is going to the gym. I want to go with him.

_____

3. We could use the treadmill. We could use the weights.

_____

4. I could be as strong as Ben. I don't work out regularly.

_____

5. Tammi likes to play hockey best. Sometimes she plays soccer.

_____

6. Tammi likes to play goalie. Andy likes to be a forward

_____

7. Let's go outside and practice. We could watch sports on TV.

_____

8. I love to play sports. I like to watch them, too.

_____

57 ©1999 School Zone Publishing Company

Dictionary: Entries and Entry Words

Dictionaries list the meanings, pronunciations, and parts of speech of words. The words that are defined in dictionaries, the entry words, appear in alphabetical order. Look at the **entry**, the **entry word**, and the information about it, for the word *dribble*.

entry word

pronunciation

part of speech

example sentence

entry

part of speech

drib•ble (drib´əl) **verb 1** to flow in drops or a trickle. *Water dribbled from the pipe.* **2** in basketball or soccer, to control the ball while kicking or bouncing it. — **drib´bled drib´bling** — **noun 1** a small drop. **2** the act of dribbling a ball.

Now examine this entry.

scheme (skēm) **noun 1** a plan in which things are carefully put together. *the color scheme of a house.* **2** a plan or program, often secret or dishonest. *a scheme for getting people to give money.* **verb** to make secret dishonest plans; to plot. *Sue is always scheming to avoid her homework.* — **schemed, schem´ing — schem´er noun**

1. Which parts of speech can *scheme* be? _____

2. How many syllables does *scheme* have? _____

3. Does *scheme* rhyme with *beam* or *hem*?_____

4. Use the word *scheme* as a verb in a sentence. _____

_____

©1999 School Zone Publishing Company

Dictionary: Guide Words

Guide words help you find entry words in a dictionary. Guide words tell you the first and last words on a dictionary page. The other words on the page are in alphabetical order between these words.

entry word

entry word

cheetah	107	chicken

chee•tah (chē tə) **noun 1** a swift leopard-like animal of Africa and South Asia

chess (ches) **noun 1** a game played on a checkerboard by two players

You would expect to find the entry words *cherry, chest,* and *chew* on this page because all three words fall alphabetically between *cheetah* and *chest.* But you would not find the words *cheese* or *child* on this page. *Cheese* comes before *cheetah* in the alphabet and *child* comes after *chest.*

Write the words from the word box that you would find on a dictionary page with the guide words *snail* and *snowfall.*

snail	565	snowfall

sniff
snack
snowstorm
snuggle
sneak
snapshot

sneeze
snake
snore
snarl
snowplow
snorkel

1. _____

2. _____

3. _____

4. _____

5. _____

6. _____

7. _____

8. _____

©1999 School Zone Publishing Company

Dictionary: Pronunciation Key

A **pronunciation key** in a dictionary shows you how to pronounce entry words.

Pronunciation Key

a	add	i	it	o͞o	pool
ā	ace	ī	ice	u	up
â	care	o	odd	û	burn
ä	palm	ō	open	yo͞o	fuse
e	end	ô	order	oi	oil
ē	equal	o͝o	took		

ə = { **a** in *above*   **e** in *sicken*   **i** in *possible*
       o in *melon*   **u** in *circus*

Look at each phonetic spelling. Use the pronunciation key to decide which of the three words it spells. Write the word in the blank.

1. (al´i ḡa´tər) (allergy, alibi, alligator) _____

2. (as´tə roid´) (asterisk, asteroid, astonish) _____

3. (bliz´ərd) (blister, blizzard, blazer) _____

4. (gi tär´) (gutter, guitar, gather) _____

5. (mag´nit) (magnet, magic, magazine) _____

6. (prə pel´ər) (property, propeller, properly) _____

7. (sat´ərn) (Saturday, sudden, Saturn) _____

8. (snāk) (snack, sink, snake) _____

Answers

Page 1
1. yes
2. no
3. yes
4. yes
5. no
6. no
7. yes
8. no
9. no
10. yes

Page 2
underline:
1. Mr. Ramirez   s
2. The band   s
3. Cory and Rosa   c
4. Jeannette   s
5. Leroy and his brother   c
6. The bus   s
7. Our driver   s
8. Mia and I   c
9. Parents and students   c
10. They   s

Page 3
1. crawled out of the ocean   s
2. dug in the sand and laid her eggs   c
3. covered the eggs with sand   s
4. shone on the sand and warmed the eggs   c
5. dug up an egg and ate it   c
6. took some eggs for soup   s
7. finally hatched   s
8. climbed out of the sand   s
9. ran down the sand and swam into the sea   c
10. will come back and lay eggs   c

Page 4
1. I like pizza, but I hate mushrooms on it.
2. Greg dislikes pizza, and he doesn't like hot dogs either.
3. not a compound sentence
4. Dee makes her own pizza sauce, but she buys crust.
5. Pizza has a lot of fat calories, but it sure is good.
6. My mom doesn't eat pizza, and neither does my dad.
7. not a compound sentence

Page 5
1. .
2. .
3. .
4. ?
5. ?
6. ?
7. .
8. .
9. .
10. ?

Page 6
1. Don't give away the ending to the movie.
2. Yikes, it's an alien!
3. Wow, I was really scared!
4. Tell your friend what time the movie starts.
5. Pay for the popcorn at the food stand.
6. Oh, gross, there's gum on my shoe!
7. Cover your eyes at the scary parts.

Page 7
circle:
1. *star patterns*
   Constellations are patterns of stars.
2. *just after sunset*
   Dusk is the time of day just after the sun sets.
3. *shooting his bow and arrow*
   An archer is a person who shoots a bow and arrow.
4. *brighter and dimmer*
   To shimmer is to get brighter and dimmer.
5. *unbelievable*
   Incredible means *unbelievable.*
6. *Earth, eight other planets, and the sun.*
   A solar system is a star with planets around it.

Page 8
1. a pig and a spider
2. The second paragraph should be circled.
3. The book report writer likes the characters and the information about animals.

Page 9
Responses will vary.

Page 10
Responses will vary.

Page 11
James and the Giant Peach
Roald Dahl
Delete sentence 4 and the last sentence.
Other responses will vary.

Page 12
Responses will vary.

Page 13
underline:
1. west
2. arm
3. brother, hospital
4. hospital, doctor, cast
5. home
6. dog
7. uncle, skis
8. bike

Person	Place	Animal	Thing
brother	west	dog	arm
doctor	hospital		cast
uncle	home		skis
			bike

Page 14
1. trucks
2. guys, crates
3. bananas
4. clerks, customers
5. apples, oranges
6. lemons
7. pies, cakes
8. grapes
9. dollars
10. pears

Page 15
1. buses, classes
2. boxes, lunches
3. dishes, glasses
4. stories
5. butterflies, branches, bunnies

©1999 School Zone Publishing Company

Answers

Page 16
1. Miss Sampson asked about our summer vacations.
2. Teddy and Barb showed pictures of the Everglades.
3. The Tafts liked Florida better than Texas.
4. Leroy saw wolves at Yellowstone Park.
5. Eli and the Cohens went canoeing in Michigan.
6. Roger's dad, Doctor Madison, helped a sick camper.
7. Randy and Maria loved the Grand Canyon.
8. The Gurwitzes just escaped Hurricane George.

Page 17
1. Thursday
2. Halloween
3. summer
4. Monday
5. New Year's Day
6. birthday
7. weekend
8. Fourth of July
9. April
10. Thanksgiving

Page 18
1. Dr., St.
2. Jr., T.L.
3. Mr., Ms., Ave.
4. G.P., Blvd.
5. Gen., Mrs.
6. Mr., Mrs., St., Ct.

Page 19
1. kangaroo's
2. rabbit's
3. Kangaroos'
4. marsupials'
5. mother's
6. mammals'
7. baby's
8. Australia's

Page 20
1. b
2. a
3. b
4. a

Exact wording of answers will vary.
5. kind of toy, highest
6. want, lengthy or not short
7. puts behind or drops, things that grow on trees
8. look out for, timepiece worn on wrist

Page 21
1. C.   2. B.
3. A.   4. B.
5. C.   6. A.
7. B.   8. A.
9. B.   10. C.

Page 22
1. has
2. had
3. has
4. has
5. has
6. have
7. have
8. have

Page 23
1. present
2. present
3. present
4. past
5. past
6. present
7. past
8. past

Page 24
1. present
2. past
3. past
4. past
5. present
6. present
7. present
8. present
9. present
10. present

Page 25
1. Our class will start a school garden.
2. We will spend time in our garden each week.
3. We think the flowers will make the schoolyard pretty.
4. We also will grow vegetables in the garden.
5. We will give some vegetables to feed hungry people.
6. Suni will plant beans.
7. I will pick peas, and Grant will dig carrots.
8. We all will weed the garden regularly.

Page 26
1. went
2. come
3. see, do
4. ran
5. ate, came
6. go
7. came
8. ate, did
9. eat
10. came

Page 27
1. The writer does not want an office building built in the park.
2. ruin the park
3. The park is a place for animals to live. It is a place for people to do many things.
4. come to the City Council meeting, and try to save the park

Page 28
Responses will vary.

Page 29
Responses will vary.

Page 30
I believe Jan Parker should be elected student council president. She listens to everybody and has good leadership qualities. Who could do a better job?

Delete sentences 4 and 8

Page 31
Responses will vary.

Page 32
The class is studying animals. We saw a movie about snakes today. I don't know why people are frightened of snakes. They are fascinating animals. You could not race some snakes and win, since they can move seven miles per hour. We saw a big python in the movie that was as big around as a person's leg. Tania said it was really gross. But then we saw a close-up of the snake's scales. Tania said the colors and patterns were pretty. Now she thinks snakes are neat. It seems to me that snakes probably think we are the scary ones.

Sentences will vary but should include pronouns.

Page 33
1. he
2. it
3. they
4. She
5. it
6. they
7. she
8. he
9. They

Page 34
1. them
2. it
3. him
4. me
5. you
6. her
7. it

Page 35
1. I
2. me
3. me
4. I
5. me
6. me
7. I
8. I
9. me
10. I

Answers

©1999 School Zone Publishing Company

Answers

Page 36
underline:
1. my
2. his
3. their
4. theirs
5. my, her
6. our
7. ours
8. his
9. mine
10. hers

Page 37
1. "Go to warp speed!" shouted the captain.
2. "I can't," answered the first officer. "Our warp engines are down."
3. "Does anybody have any ideas?" asked the captain.
4. The engineer replied, "We could reverse the engines to push the ship backward."
5. "Try it!" ordered the captain. "We have to try everything!"
6. "It's working!" yelled the first officer.
7. "We're going backward, but the asteroid is still too close," she added.
8. Suddenly the engineer cried, "The warp engines are back up. Let's get out of here!"
9. "Please steer clear of asteroids for a while," sighed the captain. "That's an order!"
10. "Is anybody hungry?" asked the cook. "It's time for lunch."

Page 38
1. Did you read the editorial "Why Vote?" in today's paper?
2. Yes, and I liked the letter to the editor entitled "The Responsibilities of a Citizen."
3. I think "Candle in the Wind" is a very sad song.
4. But the article "The Death of a Princess" was much sadder.
5. I've always loved "Rocky Mountain High" by John Denver.
6. I prefer "Take Me Home, Country Roads" myself.
7. The poem "Steam Shovel" compares the machine to a dinosaur.
8. Yes, and the poem "Garden Hose" compares the hose to a snake.
9. There's a piece in the paper today called "Save the Park."
10. That's because last week someone wrote "Build the Mall."
11. Is "The Telltale Heart" one of Edgar Allen Poe's short stories?
12. Yes, but Jack London wrote "To Build a Fire."
Notes will vary but should use quotation marks for song and story titles.

Page 39
circle:
1. terrible
2. biggest
3. huge, excellent
4. thundering, large
5. smaller
6. adult
7. Young, muddy
8. sharp, keen
9. huge, leafy
10. meat, plant, warmer
11. gray, green
12. cooler
13. plunging
14. Some, yesterday's, today's
15. New, amazing

Page 40
circle:
1. tall, white
2. long, black
3. several, red
4. few, magic
5. famous, two, locked
6. many, heavy
7. two, huge, water
8. one
9. grand
Adjectives will vary but should describe how many and what kind.

Page 41
1. a
2. an, the
3. the, a
4. an
5. a, an
6. a
7. the
8. an, the

Page 42
1. most
2. oldest
3. highest
4. tallest, higher
5. better
6. largest
7. rare
8. strangest

Page 43
1. Jerry, Ashley, Andy
2. a mountainside in a snowstorm
3. The characters have been hiking and suddenly a storm has come up. They cannot see where they are going, and they don't know where a safe place is.

Page 44
Responses will vary.

Page 45
Responses will vary.

Page 46
"Throw it over here!" yelled Marcia.
"No, throw it here!" shouted tony. the two children were playing football with their father.
Suddenly mr. Vento tripped and fell. "Ouch," he hollered. "I think I broke my leg!"

Page 47
Responses will vary.

©1999 School Zone Publishing Company

Answers

Page 48
underline:
1. noisily (how)
2. cautiously (how)
3. sometimes (when)
4. over (where)
5. suddenly (how or when)
6. close (where)
7. playfully (how)
8. near (where)
9. loudly (how)
10. madly (how)
Sentences will vary but should include adverbs that tell how, when, and where.

Page 49
1. immediately
2. quickly
3. completely
4. promptly
5. quietly
6. extremely
7. easily
8. painfully
9. icily
10. coolly
11. impatiently
12. slowly
13. unhappily
14. safely

Page 50
1. adjective
2. adverb
3. adjective
4. adjective
5. adverb
6. adverb
7. adjective
8. adjective
9. adverb
10. adverb
11. adjective
12. adjective

Page 51
1. inside
2. down
3. everywhere
4. behind
5. ahead
6. away
7. outside
8. close
9. there, up
10. inside

Page 52
1. soon
2. later
3. twice
4. yesterday
5. already
6. before

Page 53
1. high, higher, highest
2. faster, fast, fastest
3. harder, hardest, hard
4. tall, taller, tallest
5. soon, soonest, sooner

Page 54
1. Nothing
2. not
3. none
4. nobody
5. No one
6. never
7. nowhere
8. None
9. no
10. not

Page 55
1. The ideas for (many common) inventions may have come from animals.
2. The turtle has (solid, armor) plates for protection. Humans use tanks that move slowly and carry soldiers safely.
3. The rattlesnake shakes its (loud) rattle if an enemy walks nearby. People can protect their homes with (noisy) alarms to warn of burglars.
4. Birds carefully avoid the (bright red) ladybug, which contains poison. (Red) signals warn traffic to stop regularly.
5. Insects and birds fly easily by rapidly beating their wings. Air moves over a wing on an airplane and causes the wing to move upward.
6. Beavers have (large, sharp) teeth for cutting down trees. People use chisels to shape wood carefully.
7. Bats make (high) sounds that bounce against (small) insects. These echoes help bats locate food instantly. People use sonar, a sound system for locating objects underwater.
8. Ducks have (soft, downy) feathers which trap layers of (warm) air. Their young can sleep comfortably. People make (special) material (in the same way) for campers to wear outside.

Page 56
1. Doesn't
2. don't
3. shouldn't
4. isn't
5. can't
6. couldn't
7. won't
8. Don't
9. Aren't
10. couldn't
11. doesn't
12. haven't

Page 57
1. Should we go skating, **or** should we play catch?
2. Ben is going to the gym, **and** I want to go with him.
3. We could use the treadmill, **or** we could use the weights.
4. I could be as strong as Ben, **but** I don't work out regularly.
5. Tammi likes to play hockey best, **but** sometimes she plays soccer.
6. Tammi likes to play goalie, **and** Andy likes to be a forward.
7. Let's go outside and practice, **or** we could watch sport on TV.
8. I love to play sports, **and** I like to watch them, too.

Page 58
1. noun and verb
2. one
3. beam
4. Sentences will vary but should include *scheme* used as a verb.

Page 59
1. snake
2. snapshot
3. snarl
4. sneak
5. sneeze
6. sniff
7. snore
8. snorkel

Page 60
1. alligator
2. asteroid
3. blizzard
4. guitar
5. magnet
6. propeller
7. Saturn
8. snake

©1999 School Zone Publishing Company Language Arts 3-4   0222